This is my house. Here is my garden.

I walk to school every day.
Goodbye, Mum! Bye, Dad!

Here is the market.

market

On Monday I come here with my dad.
We buy apples and bananas.

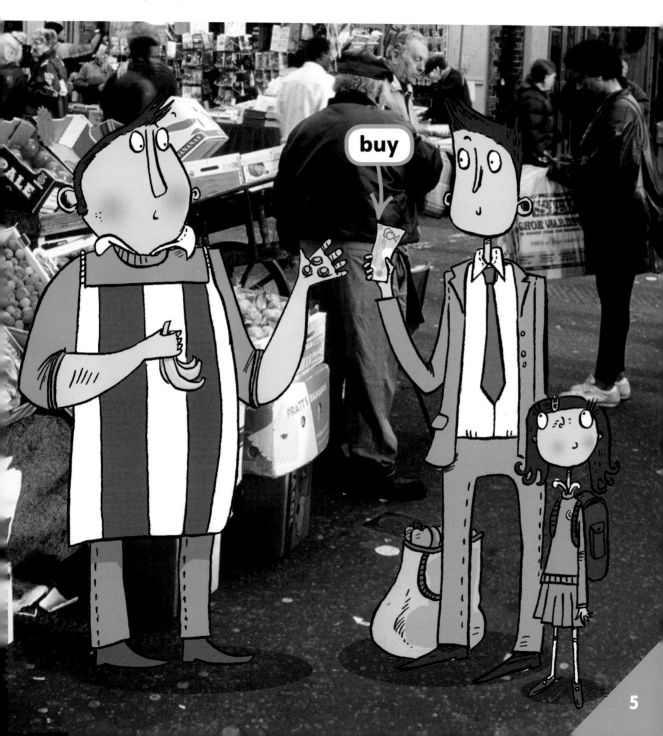

Here is the pet shop.

On Tuesday I come here with my grandfather.
We give the cats some food.

Here is the tea shop.

tea shop

On Wednesday I come here with my mum.
We eat cake!

Here is the park.

On Thursday I come here with my brother.
We run and play!

Here is my school. I come here every day.

I see my friends and my teacher.
Good morning, Miss Brown!

I love my neighbourhood!

Activities

Before You Read

1 **Match the words and pictures.**

market   tea shop   park   school   pet shop   house

After You Read

1 **Read and match to the places in Activity 1.**

1   I run and play here.
2   I give the cats food here.
3   I eat cake here.
4   I see my friends and my teacher here.
5   I buy apples and bananas here.
6   I live here.

2 **Read. Write yes (Y) or no (N).**

1   Emma goes to school every day.
2   Emma goes to the market on Tuesday.
3   Emma goes to the pet shop with her grandfather.
4   Emma goes to the tea shop on Wednesday.
5   Emma goes to the park on Monday.

Pearson Education Limited
Edinburgh Gate, Harlow,
Essex CM20 2JE, England
and Associated Companies throughout the world.

ISBN: 978-1-4082-8820-7

This edition first published by Pearson Education Ltd 2013
1 3 5 7 9 10 8 6 4 2
Text copyright © Pearson Education Ltd 2013

Set in 19/23pt OT Fiendstar
Printed in China
SWTC/01

Acknowledgements
The publisher would like to thank the following for their kind permission to reproduce their photographs:
(Key: b-bottom; c-centre; l-left; r-right; t-top)

Alamy Images: Alan Copson City Pictures 4-5, 15 (c), Mark Carper 10-11, 15 (d),
Loop Images Ltd 8-9, 15 (b), T.M.O.Buildings 6-7, 15 (f), Maria Wachala 2-3, 14, 15 (a),
Richard Wayman 1; **Getty Images**: Echo 13; **Rex Features**: Susannah Ireland 12, 15 (e)
Cover images: *Front*: **Alamy Images**: Maria Wachala

All other images © Pearson Education

In some instances we have been unable to trace the owners of copyright material,
and we would appreciate any information that would enable us to do so.

Illustrations: Sarah Horne (Advocate)

Published by Pearson Education Ltd in association with
Penguin Books Ltd, both companies being subsidiaries of Pearson Plc

For a complete list of the titles available in the Penguin Kids series please go to www.penguinreaders.com.
Alternatively, write to your local Pearson Education office or to: Penguin Readers Marketing Department,
Pearson Education, Edinburgh Gate, Harlow, Essex CM20 2JE, England.